Melting Snow

Story by Linda Strachan
Pictures by Arlene Adams

OXFORD
UNIVERSITY PRESS

"It's snowing. Let's make a snowman!"

Everyone came out to make
a snowman.

"I want to make the head," said Tom.

"I want to make the body," said Joe.

5

Everyone helped to make the snowman. It got **bigger** and **bigger**.

The sun came out and the
snow began to melt.

Our snowman got smaller and smaller.

The rain came down
and more snow
melted.

Our snowman got smaller and smaller.

Our snowman melted away.
Everyone was sad.

Mum made some
new snowmen.

They were
smaller than
our snowman.

Everyone got a little snowman.

They all melted away!